ENJOY ' BOOK !

The Mud Hole

By Arthur Brood

Illustrated by Lindsey Bergsma

Class Act Productions

www.classactproductions.us

The Mud Hole

No part of this book may be used or reproduced in any manner without written permission except in the case of brief quotations embodied in critical articles and reviews.

All characters and events are fictional. Any similarities to actual events, and/or any person, living or dead, is coincidental and unintended.

For further information, contact Class Act Productions at the website below.

www.classactproductions.us

ISBN 978-0-9794851-0-7

To my wife, Karen, who spent countless hours editing the text and encouraging me to write the book. To my daughters, Rebecca and Hannah, who shared the excitement in my writing and included parts of the story in their play.

Contents

1. Mud! Mud! Mud!

Springtime! In Pine Springs this meant a boy's paradise. Streams made from melting snow, ditches filled with water up to the knees, water-logged pastures, and oozing mud could be seen for miles in every direction. To a boy in Pine Springs, this meant countless hours of fun and adventure after the final school bell rang and before evening chores began.

Henry and Robert Morrison were two of the boys in Pine Springs who loved water and mud. On any given springtime day, the two brothers could be seen standing in the middle of the road, both with a stick or shovel in their hand and a gleam of possibilities in their big brown eyes. Henry, being ten years old and a little more than two years older than his brother, was usually the one who was the first to find mischief. On one spring day, he was standing in mud that came almost to the top of his boots.

"Mud! I've seen nothing but white for months and now all I see is mud!" exclaimed a very excited Henry.

"It's better than snow!" Robert replied as he stuck his tongue through the hole left by a lost tooth.

"Robert!" Henry called to his younger brother, "Dig a ditch to move that water over to this little mud hole and maybe we can make a small lake." The mud splattered on their faces, nearly matching the color of their hair, as they poked the soft mud with sticks to make small rivers and lakes.

"Yeah! Maybe we can use some twigs as boats and sail them down to the lake," Robert replied. Robert knew that Henry would never pass by a challenge to race imaginary boats made from nature's abundant supply of sticks, bark, or any other floatable object.

In no time at all, Henry and Robert were crouched beside the streams of water churning through boy made dikes and dams cheering on their racing boats to the finish line. First one boat and then the other would take the lead. As the boats sailed under the designated willow branch, Henry and Robert heard their father in the distance calling them to feed the horses.

"Just when we were getting the water flowing really good too," Robert complained as they walked toward the barn.

The weathered gray barn was not very large, but it was like a castle for the two boys on rainy days. The cedar shingled roof pointed to the sky, and the loft where hay was stored for the animals provided many places to hide from their sister, Elizabeth. Even the stable below seemed like a dungeon for their mysterious adventures. The only place they could not play was in Pa's workshop which was a lean-to attached to the side of the barn.

"What were you two scheming today?" asked Pa when they finally reached the stable.

Henry and Robert were usually up to some mischief, and the looks on their faces indicated their activity had been interrupted by feeding time.

"You're going to need to build a boat with all of the spring runoff this year," Pa said as his boots sloshed through the mud in the barnyard. "If I know you two rascals it could turn into a real adventure like flying your sled plane," Pa said with a twinkle in his eye.

Henry's cheeks instantly blushed red and his eyes focused on the cracks in the floorboards rather than on his father's face. He remembered just a few weeks back when he and his brother tried to attach wings to the toboggan. Henry had seen a drawing of an airplane being launched off a ramp in a book his grandpa had about physical science. Their goal had been to get enough speed down the big hill so that when they hit the snow ramp they had built, it would send them flying. They flew all right, no more than 10 feet, and then landed with a crash that broke the toboggan into enough kindling to light fires for an entire month. He and Robert had come out a little bruised up, too. Pa wasn't very happy at first, but had teased them about it since the crash landing. Ma on the other hand was convinced that they were going to end up having a funeral by spring.

"Thinking about those automobile con-traptions again?" The question from his father snapped Henry's mind back into the present.

"Not this time Pa," he replied.

"This is a moment to write down," Pa responded with a little teasing in his voice, "my Henry not thinking about those noisy, smelly automobiles."

"Pa, why do you call them noisy and smelly all the time?" Henry asked. "You need to use your imagination along with your nose and ears."

Pa leaned against the pitchfork he'd been using to clean out the horse stalls and stated seriously, "I can hear an automobile five minutes before it passes by, and I can smell it five minutes after it's gone."

"But Pa, I can smell the horse manure for thirty minutes after I clean the horse stalls," Henry retorted, "and the sound of an automobile is like music to my ears."

"It might be music to your ears, but it is nothing but noise in the peaceful countryside," Pa chided.

Pa's statement brought an end to the automobile discussion. The remainder of chore time was done in the peace and quiet that Pa so enjoyed. As father and sons worked side by side, their ears filled with the sounds of hay crunching underfoot, milk streaming into buckets, and the contented sounds of the barn animals enjoying their supper. The only sound that disturbed Henry was his growling stomach as he thought ahead to his own supper. Chores, supper, a little while to whittle away on the boat he was carving from the pine branch he'd found in the meadow last fall, and then it would be time for bed. With no one to interrupt his thoughts, Henry could dream to his heart's content about owning and driving his own automobile one-day.

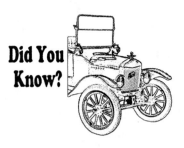

Early automobiles were fairly simple. In 1912 they were considered noisy and smelly to most people who had lived their lives in the quiet countryside. Over time, many inventions have been developed that have reduced the noise and smells coming from an automobile.

2.   Spring Thaw

The countryside looked eerie with the morning frost clinging to every twig on every tree. The frost hardened the ground making it easy to walk the three miles to school.

The school, built just two years before in 1910, was a small one-room schoolhouse with white siding. It was the first building on the edge of Pine Springs. School used to meet in the church, but students were distracted by the sounds coming from the general store next door.

The day at school was uneventful as spring was in the air and all the students were beginning to get a strong case of spring fever. Every student was looking forward to the end of the school day and the chance to be outside. Henry also looked forward to the two-mile journey home that by the afternoon would turn into a challenging route.

The journey home from school became challenging because Henry and his brother and sister had to walk on the road. The morning frost had gone with the rising of the sun. In the warm afternoon sunshine, the spring thaw continued to melt the snow and create mud everywhere.

The road was a mess as horse and wagons had created ruts along most of the two-mile journey. Those who owned automobiles did not dare take their autos out on country roads during the spring thaw. They knew good and well they would spend more time getting the auto out of the mud then they would driving down the road. Henry remembered last spring when Mr. Johnson had attempted to drive down a street in town with his Ford Model T only to have it stuck in mud so deep it came to the bottom of the fenders. It had cost him three whole dollars to get pulled out of the gooey mud. It took him three whole months to stop being the object of laughter in town when people teased him and told him, "Get a horse!" Since then, the wise automobile owners waited to drive until the ground dried up after the spring thaw choosing to slosh through the mucky mire on foot or by horse in the mean time.

The biggest challenge of each day for Henry, Robert and Elizabeth was to get past the mud hole that was a hundred yards before the family farm. It was near the creek at the bend in the road. Thick trees and shrubbery on both sides of the road made it nearly impossible to walk around it. Henry considered the mud hole challenge the best part of the walk home, as did Robert. Elizabeth, however, was a different story. At seven years old she was more interested in keeping her dress clean than wading through mud.

Henry and Robert had tired of her complaining and had schemed a plan together. At the edge of the mud hole, Elizabeth climbed on to Henry's back while Robert helped to steady Henry. Midway through the mud, Henry acted like he started to slip. Extending his hand and acting like he was trying to help, Robert bumped Henry and knocked Elizabeth off of Henry's back and into the mud.

"AHHH!" Elizabeth wailed. "I'm telling Ma and Pa what you did!" She threatened in an angry voice. Covered from head to toe in mud, Elizabeth stomped off to the house as Henry and Robert, with smirks on their faces, quickly scampered away and hid behind the barn. No matter if they got in trouble, both boys agreed that it had been a very rewarding day at the mud hole.

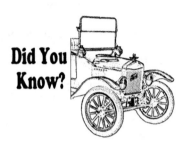

Roads in the country during this period of time were dirt. Sometimes they were just two-track trails. These roads may have begun as old wagon trails used by early settlers and explorers. Other roads began as trails used by Native Americans. Other roads were made to go around a physical object like a lake, river, swamp or large hill. The roads were not usually maintained to remove bumps or fill in mud holes.

Two-track trails: A road that has a long width of dirt for each wheel with grass growing in between.

3.   Mr. Johnson's Model T

School always ended in the spring as soon as the snow was off of the fields because living on a farm meant each family member was expected to help with the spring planting. Life on the farm meant working on the farm. School was important, but getting the farm work done was survival because each farmer raised food for his family for the next year. Pa and Ma worked together to get everything accomplished and they expected all three of their children to help according to each one's ability. With all of the planting, gardening, harvesting, canning, and chores, it was hard to find time to do the fun things Henry wanted to do.

Even though the snow was gone and the roads were mostly dry, the mud hole near

Henry's house was still a mucky mess. A mucky, messy, mud hole was a problem for everyone except Henry and Robert. Even with all of the responsibilities on the farm, they still found time to play in the mud.

Although the mud hole was a favorite place to play for Henry and his brother, it was a great irritation to their Pa. Just yesterday, he had needed to come in from working the fields to pull a motorist from the mud hole not once or twice, but three times. Pa was always friendly to the owner of the stranded automobile, but by the third time, Henry knew his Pa was becoming frustrated. Normally Pa charged two dollars to pull out a motorist, but the third unlucky fellow was charged three dollars.

Any unlucky motorist who did not know to stay on the left side of the mud hole always became stuck. Since there were no other houses for the next half-mile up the road, Pa was always the one to be called to the rescue. Henry and

Robert loved this arrangement, but for Pa it was nothing less than irritating.

"Henry," Pa called, "I need two more bushels of corn to finish planting the field on the ridge. I was interrupted so many times yesterday by those flimsy auto contraptions getting stuck in the mud hole that I didn't have time to go to the mill and get more seed. I want you to take the riding horse and get me two bushels of corn."

Henry's mind was spinning with excitement. Mr. Johnson lived right next to the mill and if he was lucky he would get to see Mr. Johnson's Ford Model T. Mr. Johnson kept the black paint so shiny it looked like the night sky. Then when you looked into the brass headlights and radiator you could see your reflection. Henry had laid awake at nights dreaming of getting a ride in Mr. Johnson's Ford Model T. He could almost feel the air rushing past his face as he imagined riding with the top of the car folded back. Even though Mr. Johnson kept the car so clean it wasn't the fanciest car Henry had seen, but that didn't matter. It had a motor and could be driven without a horse.

"Henry?" Pa broke into Henry's thoughts, "Are you going to the mill or are you going to keep standing there all day dreaming of automobile contraptions?"

"I'm doing a disappearing act right now," Henry said as he was jolted back from his imagination. "Hey, Pa, do you think Mr. Johnson will give me a ride in his Ford Model T today?" Henry called back as he ran to saddle the riding horse.

"Not if you stand here dreaming all day," Pa teased.

Henry arrived in town and found Mr. Johnson with a bucket of water and a cloth wiping mud off of the hood of his Ford Model T. "Good morning, Mr. Johnson!" Henry greeted.

"It would be a much better morning if that blasted mud hole by your Pa's farm would dry up," retorted Mr. Johnson. "I have to go into that mud hole pretty fast so I can make it through without getting stuck. Mud ends up on everything. It seems as if I spend just as much time washing this machine as I do driving it!" complained Mr. Johnson as he poured a bucket of water over the hood.

Henry did not like how this conversation was going and realized today was not the day to ask for a ride in the Model T. "It is quite a mud hole," Henry replied cautiously. "Yesterday, Pa had to pull three motorists from it. There was a red one called a Maxwell, and the driver was wearing a driving mask and goggles." Henry continued on, "He said it keeps the dust and mud out of his face when he is driving fast."

Mr. Johnson just grunted at Henry's news. He went back to washing his automobile while Henry continued riding the horse to the mill. Henry completed the errand for his pa and on the way home thought about Mr. Johnson washing his

Model T. Suddenly a grin came on Henry's face as a plan came to his mind.

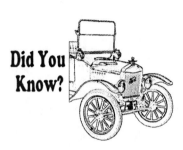

Did You Know?

Many ideas and developments came as a result of the automobile. One of these ideas was the gas station. Before the invention of the gas station, gasoline had to be purchased at a hardware or general store.

4.   A Not So Good Idea

When Henry got home he found Robert in the barn hayloft.

"Robert!" Henry shouted, "I have an idea!"

"What this time?" came the wary reply.

"It's like this," began Henry, "You know that mud hole down the road a piece? Whenever an automobile goes through the mud it comes out muddy, right? We can wash the automobiles as they come out and keep the drivers happy."

Robert wasn't so sure, but he was willing to listen to his brother's idea.

Henry continued, "We climb a tree and when they come out of the mud we dump a bucket of water on the automobile. Comes out clean as a whistle."

Later that day, Henry and Robert were busy finding an empty bucket and some extra rope. The only part of the plan that took some time to solve was finding the right tree, but when they finally found the tree it was perfect. It was a big oak with large branches that hung over the road. It would be easy to sit on the large limbs to empty the buckets of water on the autos driving underneath. Robert followed Henry with his eyes as he watched his brother shinny up the tree to the lowest overhanging branch.

"Are you sure this is a good idea? Robert asked with some doubt in his voice.

"Why wouldn't it be a good idea?" Henry answered as he inched further out onto the branch.

"What if they don't want their car washed?" Robert thought out loud.

"Hey, silly brother," Henry teased, "who wants to have a dirty automobile? Every automobile driven into this mud hole comes out dirty.

We clean it for them as they drive under the tree. Ta-dah, a clean auto again and a happy driver!"

"I know why we need a bucket, but why do we need a rope and tree to wash the dirty automobiles?" Robert doubtfully asked.

"It's like this," Henry called down to his brother, "you go fill the bucket with water from the creek, tie the handle to the rope, and then I'll pull the bucket up into the tree. Once the bucket is up, then you climb on up. When the automobile drives under the tree we dump the water out of the bucket and it washes the mud from the automobile."

A short time later both boys were hiding in the tree waiting for their first customer. It didn't take long for a little Oldsmobile Runabout to come splashing through the mud hole.

"Washing number one!" called Henry. When the little car was underneath the tree Henry dumped the bucket of water and watched as the little Oldsmobile sped by without a drop of water touching it.

"You missed!" Robert teased.

"I forgot that it takes a little time for the water to fall to the ground," Henry answered, somewhat embarrassed about his mistake. He sent Robert for another bucket of water while he tried to figure out the timing for dumping the water so it hit the automobile at the right moment.

Thirty minutes later a bright red Maxwell with wood spoke wheels came through the mud hole. "Ready? Now!" Henry spoke as the bucket of water spilled on the little car that had no top.

A scream from the driver confirmed that the water had made contact with the automobile. A moment later, the Maxwell slid to a stop and a startled driver came huffing back to the tree.

"What in blazes are you boys doing?", screamed the angry driver. "Get down here this minute so I can take you to your parents and explain what you have done."

Henry was trying not to laugh as he looked down on the wet driver who was steaming mad and looked incredibly silly. Robert was a little more scared and was the first to speak, "Henry, we didn't think about getting the driver wet."

"You didn't think about getting the driver wet?" fumed the angry driver. "Just what were you trying to do then?"

Henry started sensing the trouble he was in and quietly replied, "We were trying to help motorists clean their automobile after driving through the mud hole."

The short walk to the house was not pleasant with the angry driver making threats by their side the entire way. Henry and Robert knew, without a doubt, they were in big trouble.

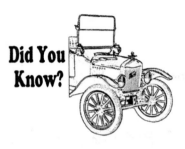

Did You Know?

Automobiles during this time period were almost all open topped, although they were not called convertibles yet. Some automobiles had a canvas top that could be put up while others did not. A bucket of water dumped into an automobile would not be a good experience for the driver.

5. The Job is Yours

Henry survived the discipline he received for washing unsuspecting motorists. In addition to his regular chores, he was assigned extra farm work for two weeks. There was very little time left in Henry's day to go looking for adventure by the time his work was completed. However, in the moments he had time to think, Henry had schemed a bunch of things he wanted to do, if he ever got time.

Following the two weeks of discipline, Henry was very happy to see that the mud hole had not gone away. It seemed to rain just enough during the spring to keep it from drying up. Pa, on the other hand, was getting more and more irritated because every time a motorist got stuck he would show up on the porch requesting assistance from pa's horse.

"Henry! Robert!" Pa called them over one day. "I'll never get the work done around the farm with these blasted motorists getting stuck all the time. Henry, you've not only taken a fancy to those automobile contraptions, you're big enough now to handle the horse. From now on, when those stranded motorists set foot on this porch asking for assistance, you and Robert can have the job!"

"You really mean that Pa?" Henry asked.

"Yep! Now remember, I charge them two dollars to get pulled out. The two of you can share the money, but you need to buy the feed for the horse out of whatever money you make."

Henry was so excited he nearly didn't hear the rest of what his Pa was saying. He would get to see each and every vehicle up close and talk with all of the drivers. Life couldn't get any better than this!

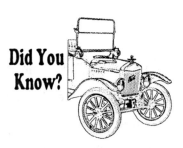

Did You Know?

There were no tow trucks in 1912. People traveling with automobiles had to rely on a nearby farmer with a horse to be helped out of a mud hole. If an automobile broke down the driver either had to fix it on his or her own, or have the vehicle dragged into town by a horse to find someone who could. It has been said that a common fix for a leaky *radiator* was to crack an egg and pour it into the radiator. The yoke of the egg would gel and seal the leak.

Radiator: A part of the automobile holding water that is used to cool the engine.

6. The First Customer

Later in the afternoon, while Henry, Robert, and Elizabeth were helping their mother in the garden, a strange creature came walking up the driveway. The general shape was that of a man, but the clothing he had on almost made Henry wonder if he was human.

On his head he had a tight leather hat that tied around his chin. It fit tightly and started just above the eyebrows going over the ears and down to the collar of the coat in the back. It made the mysterious man appear to have no hair. He had goggles that were pushed up on his forehead making it look like the man had four eyes on his head. He wore a long coat that hung just below his knees, which was covered with mud.

Henry's eyes flashed. This was it! His first customer! Henry jumped up so fast the weeds he'd been pulling went flying all over the garden. Before the driver was halfway up the lane, Henry was at his side asking if he needed any sort of help.

"Well, is your Pa home? My automobile seems to be stuck down the road a piece and I need a horse to pull it out," the stranger replied.

"Pa would tell you to buy a horse," Henry laughed. "My Pa's asked me and my brother to pull out motorists who get stranded in the mud because we like automobiles and he has work to do. Let me get our horse, Sally, and I'll be right down."

"Much obliged," said the stranger.

At the mud hole Henry saw an amazing site. Stuck in the mud was no Model T or little Oldsmobile that were the common victims trapped in the mud hole. This was one, long, beautiful machine. It had huge brass headlights

that stuck out from the front of the automobile.
The tires, from what Henry and Robert could see
through the mud, were large white walled tires
on wood spoked wheels.

"What kind of automobile is that?" Henry
asked in awe.

"That is one, stuck Pierce-Arrow," replied
the stranger.

"I've never heard of a Pierce-Arrow,"
Henry responded.

"I've never seen a car that long," Robert
added.

The gentle stranger quietly laughed. "I
imagine in these parts there are not too many
who could afford to buy one of these beautiful
machines." The stuck automobile looked huge to
Henry. The shiny brass headlights, although
speckled with mud, were large and polished. The
long running boards had three small, colorful cans
labeled gas, oil, and water strapped on beside the
extra tires that were there for the many flat tires

a traveler might experience. The top of the polished radiator had a hood ornament that looked like a small statue.

"Mr. Harrison, he runs the bank, doesn't even have an automobile half this nice," added Robert. "You must not be from around here. Where are you from?" Robert continued.

"Watch your manners!" Henry warned.

"It's okay" the stranger replied. "I'm from Indianapolis and I wanted to see the beautiful Michigan countryside I've heard about."

"INDIANAPOLIS!" both boys interrupted at the same time. "That's not even in Michigan!"

Henry went on to say, "I've heard that it could take two days to get to Indianapolis by train. I can't even imagine how long it would take by horse and carriage. How long has it taken you to drive this far in your Pierce-Arrow?"

"Well, my wife and I have been driving for five and a half days, but we haven't been in much of a hurry."

Henry and Robert had been so distracted by the automobile's size and the conversation with the stranger, that they had not noticed a passenger sitting in the stuck Pierce-Arrow. Just then a lady opened the door of the automobile wearing one of the silliest masks Henry and Robert had ever seen. Startled both boys jumped, and then laughter started rolling from the bottom of their bellies. A moment later the stranger joined their laughter. The lady stood on the running board with a puzzled look on her face.

Henry regained his ability to talk first, "Forgive us; we don't mean to be foolish boys. We've just never seen this type of clothing before and you surprised us when you opened the door."

"Apology accepted, if you can help us out of this awful mud pit," replied the lady. "John, you told me I looked just fine after those people looked at me with odd expressions on their faces when we stopped for lunch along the side of the road. Now these two little boys outright laugh at me. Dust or not, I am not going to wear this dust mask anymore! And... John, you look absolutely foolish wearing that silly hat and motoring goggles," the lady teased with a sheepish grin.

"They are none to comfortable either. I recommend we take off the driving hat and goggles," John answered.

"I suppose it's time to give this beautiful Pierce-Arrow a pull out of the mud," Henry added. "We usually charge two dollars to pull out a car, but I will make you a deal." Henry was feeling confident with this friendly city couple. "One dollar and give us a ride in this beautiful automobile."

"Deal!" answered the stranger with a twinkle in his eye.

It wasn't long and the trees along the side of the road were beginning to blur in Henry and Robert's eyes. Dust was forming a cloud behind the speeding automobile. "I've never gone this fast in my life!" Robert exclaimed to Henry above the noise of the wind flying in their faces.

"It will go much faster," replied the stranger they only knew as John, "but the roads here are a lot rougher then by Indianapolis. A few weeks ago a friend of mine let me drive it at the 'Brickyard' in Indianapolis," explained John.

"Why would you want to drive this beautiful auto at a brickyard?" Robert was thinking of the business in town that made bricks as he asked the question.

"You must not have heard of 'THE Brick-yard.' 'The Brickyard' is Indianapolis Motor Speedway. It is a two and a half mile race track shaped in an oval and it is used for racing auto-mobiles. I was able to drive on it," John stated proudly.

"He still won't tell me how fast he drove," piped in the stranger's wife who had now taken off the silly mask and was enjoying the wind in her face.

"How fast did you go?" Henry tried to pry the answer from John.

"Fast enough I couldn't take my eyes from the road to check the speed!"

The ride ended much too soon as both boys gave their farewell with a dollar to share and an adventure they would never forget. It was the first day of what was to be a very busy summer at the mud hole.

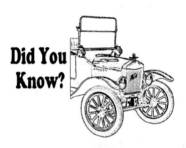

Automobiles were open topped and roads were dusty. This combination made it difficult for a driver or passenger in an automobile to stay clean. Sometimes these people would dress in strange looking clothing such as dust coats, hats and goggles to help keep the dust off.

7.   A New Plan

During the next week Henry and Robert pulled out another ten cars and earned twenty dollars, more money than they had ever seen in their lives. Henry enjoyed each and every automobile, although none were as interesting as the Pierce-Arrow. There were a few Model T's, one Oldsmobile Runabout that no longer had fenders, two open topped Maxwells and a dented up Ford Model N.

By the end of the week, however, there was almost no business for Henry and Robert. Not only was the mud hole shrinking in size from the warm summer sun, but it was becoming obvious that motorists had figured out to stay on the left side of the mud hole. Henry was concerned that pulling autos from the mud hole would soon end completely. He sat down on a log to think about this problem when a new plan started emerging in his head.

"Robert!" Henry called with two shovels in hand, "Come help me."

Robert was polishing the new glassy marbles he had won yesterday from a marble game with their neighbor, Paul. "I'm busy right now," Robert retorted. "I won 3 new glassies yesterday, but I lost my best steely in the marble game with Paul. I'm counting my marbles and figuring which ones I can use to win my steely back."

Henry dropped one shovel in front of Robert and softly whispered, "You'll be able to buy all the steelies you want if you help me."

Robert's eyes widened, "How will I do that? Pa wants us to save the money we made last week in the bank. I could have bought fifty marbles and still put money in the bank."

"I'm going to the mud hole," Henry spoke in a whisper, "and I'll tell you more when you get there."

At the mud hole, Henry laid out his latest plan for his brother. "The hole is starting to dry up and the motorists are learning to drive on the left side. We haven't pulled an automobile out in three days. I doubt we will pull out another automobile this year unless we do something. Wouldn't you like to see another Pierce-Arrow up close?"

"That was the first and probably the last Pierce-Arrow to drive down this road," Robert replied.

"But, if another one comes, don't you want to see it up close and maybe get another ride." Henry coaxed as he tried to get Robert's help in his latest plan.

Robert raised his left eyebrow, "How are we going to do that?"

The smirk on Henry's face widened, "We'll dig a little ditch from the creek over there to the mud hole. Not a big ditch, but just enough to keep water going to the mud hole and keep us in business."

Robert finally looked convinced and the two boys began digging. The shovels sliced into the moist ground as they moved the earth to allow the water to flow through. The afternoon sun beat down, and sweat rolled down their backs making their shirts sticky as they worked. After a few hours they had water trickling through a small ditch to the mud hole.

Henry was so excited about their accomplishment that he started doing a little dance right in the mud hole. Robert on the other hand, sighed, "I'm tired," as he let his shovel drop from his hand and leaned against a tree.

"Let's go to the swimming hole and clean up!" Henry suggested.

As Robert wiped sweat off his forehead he added, "And to cool off!"

Later that afternoon a thunderstorm developed and rain fell in drops the size of gumdrops. It was a warm rain and the boys splashed in puddles and played a game of tag on the way home from the swimming hole.

"This rain should help fill the mud hole too!" Robert exclaimed.

Henry just nodded his head; his plan was working just fine. It wouldn't be long and he would be back in business again and perhaps he could get another ride in a fancy automobile.

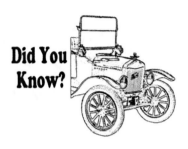

Did You Know?

Automobiles in 1912 were powered in different ways. Most were powered by using a gasoline engine, called an internal combustion engine. However, people were experimenting with other types of power during this time. Steam powered automobiles were much quieter, but it could take up to fifteen minutes or longer from the time they were started until they were ready to be driven. Electric automobiles were also being produced. They did not become popular because the batteries did not allow them to be driven long distances without being recharged.

Internal combustion engine: A type of motor that explodes fuel inside a cylinder within the motor to make power.

8. Making Money

"Thirty-six!" Henry exclaimed. "We've pulled out thirty-six automobiles since Pa let us take over the job."

"How do you know that, Henry?" questioned Robert.

"I've been keeping track of each car we've pulled out." "Let's see... one, two, three.... Henry mumbled as he counted, "twelve, thirteen, fourteen! Fourteen Model T's, four Buicks, six Oldsmobiles, three Maxwells, three Stanley Steamers, two Cadillacs, two old Ford Model N's, and the beautiful, fast Pierce-Arrow."

"Other than the Pierce-Arrow, which one did you like the best?" Robert asked.

"The fancy ones, like the Cadillac, are nice, but they're so big it would be hard to go anywhere in them. They're also a lot of car to keep clean after mud holes," Henry laughed. "So, I guess I pick the Stanley Steamer. Because it is powered by a steam engine it is quiet and doesn't smell like the other automobiles. Pa would like that."

"Yes, I would!" Pa exclaimed as both boys jumped.

"I didn't know you were standing there," a surprised Henry answered.

"Those Stanley Steamers are much more quiet than the rest of those noisy automobile contraptions. If all automobiles were as quiet as those steamers I might like them a little more." Pa went on to say, "The two of you have done very well this summer with that mud hole. If I didn't know better I would think you two spent all day hauling buckets of water down there to keep it muddy."

Robert shot a quick look at Henry. Henry shot a look back at Robert that said, "Don't you dare say a word!" even though no words were spoken.

Pa continued, "Thirty-six automobiles at two dollars a piece, lets see…."

Henry interrupted, "We only charged one dollar for three of them because they gave us a ride, and we pulled Dr. Benson out free because he had already been stuck twice before. We felt bad for him and he was on his way to an emergency."

Pa's mind was figuring. "Okay, so thirty-six times two is seventy-two, minus three dollars for the rides is sixty-nine dollars and minus two dollars for pulling out Dr. Benson for free makes sixty-seven dollars," Pa announced.

"Wow, Pa!" Henry exclaimed, "That's right! How did you do that?"

"I practiced my sums in arithmetic when I was in school; in fact I was the best in my class," Pa stated proudly.

"When I was in town today, I heard some news you boys might be interested in hearing," Pa went on to say. "The county fair is next week and they are planning to have some automobile races. I even heard that Mr. Smith wants to race his horse and cart against Mr. Johnson's Model T. I saw Mr. Johnson a little later when I was at the general store and asked him about this motorcar and horse race. He said Ned Smith needed to get his facts straight. He's not going to risk banging up his Model T racing Ned Smith. He claims Ned Smith may even run him off the track if he attempted a pass. Right about then, Herb Snider piped in and said he would race Mr. Smith. I asked him if his jalopy, whatever that automobile is called…"

"An Oldsmobile Runabout", interrupted Henry matter-of-factly.

"Well anyway, I asked if it could even make it to the track. Old Herb told me to show up and see if I was so interested. So now, boys, it sounds like there may be a motorcar and horse race at the county fair. What will they think of next?" Pa said as he started walking toward the barn.

Henry and Robert, however, let out a whoop of excitement as their minds swirled with the information their Pa had just given them. The week of the fair couldn't arrive quickly enough.

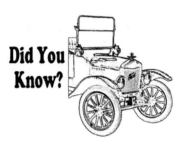

Did You Know?

In the early 1900's there were over 2000 automobile companies. Some couldn't make a profit with so much competition and went out of business. Others were bought by another company to make a larger company. General Motors is an example of several companies that were bought and combined to form one large company.

Company: A business that produces a product or provides a service for a profit.

9. The Mysterious Driver

The week seemed to drag by slowly. It was the dry part of the summer when dust hangs in the air and boys are found at the swimming hole more often then not. Even the little ditch didn't bring much water to the mud hole as only a trickle made its way through under the hot summer sun. Even with all their efforts, Henry and Robert had only helped three stranded motorists all week.

The day before the fair Henry and Robert sat on their front porch talking about the fun and excitement of the next day. Ma had given them lemonade for weeding the garden, a rare treat, which they sipped while they planned for tomorrow. While imagining the big race that was to be held, a motorist wandered up the driveway wearing one of those funny leather hats and driving goggles. Henry jumped to his feet in a heartbeat.

"I seem to be stuck in a mud hole down the road a piece," the man explained.

Upon reaching the mud hole with the driver, Henry and Robert discovered they had snared a long odd looking automobile. Unlike the Pierce-Arrow that was stuck earlier in the summer that was shiny and looked new, this automobile was dingy and banged up. It had a large number seven painted on the side of the hood, which puzzled the boys. It was also very loud. When the motorist had started the mired auto, it had startled the horse so much Robert was nearly lifted off the ground when Sally reared up on her hind legs.

Although the boys were a constant buzz of questions, the driver of this mammoth automobile was not as interested in the boys as the driver of the Pierce-Arrow automobile they had encountered earlier. Even when he did respond with a one or two word answer, he seemed distracted and in a hurry. When the mud hole finally released its grip on his auto, he quickly paid the boys and was off without even a thank you, sounding like a rumbling storm as the noisy auto disappeared over the next hill.

The boys stood there puzzling over this mysterious driver for a few minutes. Robert spoke over the drone of the motor which could still be heard in the distance, "If I had an auto like that, I wouldn't let it get so run down and smashed up as that one."

Henry reflected, "I didn't see a single part of that auto that didn't have a dent or a scratch. Why would anyone treat an auto so carelessly?

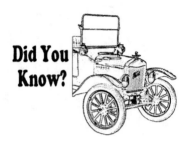

Did You Know?

As the automobile started to get older they were used in different ways around farms. Some were used to haul animals or crops such as hay to the market. Some farmers sawed wood by jacking up the rear wheels and putting the automobile in gear. The spinning rear wheels were attached to a belt powering a saw blade to cut wood. Others used it as a tractor by taking the *fenders*, doors, and windshield off when they were worn out or broken. An old car used in this way was sometimes called a *"bug"*.

Fenders: The part of the automobile that goes over the wheels and keeps mud from splashing onto other parts of the car.

Bug: The term given to a vehicle used for farm work after many parts are removed or taken off.

10. Fun At The Fair

The next morning the boys were up with the sun. Early as it was, they didn't waste a single minute as they raced to get their chores done. It was fair day!

Never had they fed and watered the livestock so quickly. Pa sternly told them to slow down after they almost collided into each other with pitchforks. However, they still finished chores in record time and were off to the fair.

Elizabeth had whined the night before that her brothers should take her with them, however, Henry and Robert had no intention of waiting around for their slowpoke sister. Fortunately, Ma had seemed to understand, and even had helped them get out of the house quietly so as not to attract attention from Elizabeth. Ma had a special way of knowing when things were really important. The fair and being with their friends were two of these things.

After reaching the fairgrounds, Henry and Robert soon had found their gang of friends from school. This was not a gang to cause problems. All of the boys knew they would be in a heap of trouble at home if they did anything to hurt anyone or damage anything, but they still enjoyed the pranks of boyhood. Ben Johnson snuck up behind Charlie MacDonald and put a frog down the back of his overalls. Later Charlie played cowboy and lassoed Ben with a rope, throwing the end of the rope over a beam in the livestock barn and lifting Ben right off of the ground.

"Hey!" Charlie exclaimed, "There's the watermelon seed spitting contest. I can spit a seed further than any of you guys."

"No you can't!" Robert retorted.

Ben gave Charlie a playful elbow in the side and said, "No way!"

"Only because you're full of hot air,"
teased Henry who didn't want to miss out on the
playful bantering.

The competition was fierce among the in-
nocent gang of boys. Charlie took such a deep
breath of air, he nearly choked on the seed
causing everyone to tease him more. Robert held
the lead for most of the game with a distance of
twelve feet four inches until his neighbor, Paul,
puckered up his cheeks and let a seed cannon out
from his lips. It sailed through the air and landed
at the feet of some of the spectators the boys
were using as targets to aim the seeds. Paul's
flying seed set a fair record of sixteen feet one
inch.

The boys stood around Paul admiring his
blue ribbon and the prize of a huge watermelon.
Although Robert would have liked to have
claimed the prize, he was a good sport and
congratulated Paul on his winnings. Suddenly

Henry called out, "Hey, guys! The greased pole climb is back this year!"

Mr. Smith was making a point of getting a good layer of grease on the pole when Henry and his friends approached. "Say, Henry! Is that mud hole nearly dried up yet?" Mr. Smith asked.

Robert flashed a worried look at Henry, but Henry kept his cool. "It seems to still catch a few motorists, Mr. Smith."

"Well, we'll see if you can climb the greased pole easier then a motorist can get through the mud hole. Do you think you can make it to the top of this pole?" Mr. Smith asked.

"I'll give it my best shot; when does it start?"

"The competition will begin fifteen minutes after the automobile races," replied Mr. Smith.

"Automobile races!" echoed a chorus of excited boy's voices. "We've been waiting a whole week to watch them! When do the races start?"

Mr. Smith chuckled, "Not long from now. The automobiles are lined up over there. I hope they don't scare too many of the animals in the livestock barns. There is one big machine that is louder than thunder. Some guy from out of town; can't remember his name right now; Bennie something. Rumor has it he goes so fast he has set a record at nearly every track at which he races."

Even before Mr. Smith finished his last sentence, the boys set off in the direction of the race track. The smell of fresh popcorn, too irresistible to pass by, made them pause as they counted out coins to each buy a bag of the special treat. However, Henry, not wanting to miss a single moment, urged the group toward the track even faster.

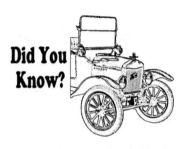

Did You Know?

To change a tire on an early automobile was quite different than today. The rim was taken off the wheel. The tire was then removed and the *inner tube* was patched. It then had to be pumped back up and put back together again. Today the *rim* and the *wheel* are one part.

Rim: The outer part of a wheel that joins the tire to the wheel.

Wheel: A part of the car that holds the tires in place and attaches to the car.

Inner Tube: An inside part of a tire that holds air.

11.   The Big Race

It didn't take long for six boys to find the small group of automobiles lined up by the track. The boys had seen most of them before. A Maxwell, Cadillac, Model T, and one that looked like the car they pulled out of the mud hole yesterday. "Hey Robert! This is the big beat up auto we pulled out of the mud hole yesterday," Henry said.

"Do you know what kind of automobile it is?" Ben asked.

Henry went on to explain that the driver of this car didn't talk much, but another kind man earlier in the summer had given the boys a ride in his beautiful Pierce-Arrow after they helped him out of the mud hole. He went on describing the automobile in such detail that the other boys were becoming a bit jealous.

"I can't believe he gave you a ride," Ben remarked.

The boys admiringly looked over each automobile two or three times until it was time for the races to begin. The voice of the announcer boomed clearly through the grand stands, "It has been reported that in New York a spectator was killed by a racing automobile because the crowd ran onto the track to get a closer look. For your safety we ask that all spectators stay in the grand stand area. We will stop all events if any spectators come onto the track area."

The first event featured a horse against an Oldsmobile Runabout. The Runabout was ten years old and wasn't very quick. It was able to reach a speed of about twenty miles per hour and could keep going at that speed as long as the road was smooth. The crowd hushed as the race began and the horse galloped out to an early lead. The little Oldsmobile coughed and sputtered but soon the engine smoothed out and a trail of dust drifted lazily behind. It appeared the horse and rider would soon lap the little Oldsmobile as they were coming out of the turn on the left side of the track just as the sputtering little automobile was entering the turn on the right side of the track. However, it was now the fourth lap of the race. The steady rhythm of the horse hooves slowed as the sweat-covered stallion grew tired, allowing the Oldsmobile to slowly catch up. As the horse and rider approached the finish line, with the little Oldsmobile a short fifty yards behind, the spectators in the grandstands who were still loyal to horse and buggy transportation started chanting, "GET A HORSE! GET A HORSE!"

Once the loyal horse owners finally settled down the announcer began again, "It is our good fortune today to have with us a pioneer in automobile racing, Beeennniiie Sanderson!" The announcer stretched out Bennie's name and then had to pause for the crowd's cheering and applause. After the noise died down he began again. "Bennie began his racing on bicycles before the turn of the century, but soon found he needed the speed only found in automobiles. He is driving a Peerless Green Dragon racecar that was once raced by Barney Oldfield, the legendary racer who helped Henry Ford into the automo-bile business. Bennie has broken speed records on more tracks than I could count using my fingers and toes. Ladies and Gentlemen, please welcome Bennie Sanderson!"

As the crowd began to clap and cheer again, the noise of thunder vibrated through the air. Henry and the other boys instantly looked toward the sky to look for storm clouds, but in fact the skies were clear. The noise had not come from the sky at all; Bennie had started his racer.

Henry looked at Robert. Above the roar of the automobile he shouted, "Can you believe it? We pulled Bennie Sanderson out of the mud hole. I almost feel as if I'm in heaven!"

True to his reputation, at the crack of the starting gun the wheels on Bennie's racer began throwing dirt and Bennie launched from the starting line roaring around the track. The competitors didn't stand a chance. The dust rose from the track creating a fog of dust that engulfed the grandstand area. The dust hovering over the track made it difficult to see when Bennie Sanderson came around the last curve. The boys whooped and hollered with the cheering crowd as the announcer proclaimed Bennie Sanderson the winner as the racecar roared in front of the grandstands leaving the rest of the automobiles far behind in the dust.

Henry and his friends slithered like a snake through the crowd to where Bennie Sanderson was climbing out of his car.

"That was a great race!" Henry commented toward Bennie, "I didn't know you were a racer when I pulled you from the mud hole yesterday."

Bennie was wiping the layers of dust from his face and had put his racing goggles on his head making him look like a bug. "You're the kid who helped me out of that mud hole, Thanks! I'm sorry for not saying so at the time. Yesterday wasn't a very good day for me as I had two tires blow out and I got stuck in that mud hole. I'm afraid I wasn't really friendly at that point of the day. Say, did you boys enjoy the race?"

"I've never seen anything go so fast," blurted Charlie.

"You boys can go ahead and sit up on the seat if you like. Just don't touch the exhaust pipe, because I don't want you burned. Don't try cranking it, either!" Bennie added with a twinkle in his eye.

Henry couldn't imagine a better ending to a perfect day. Nothing else at the fair was as exciting as sitting in the automobile that won the race. Not even the grease pole!

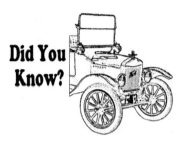

Early races involving the automobile were dangerous. Crowds often stood on the track to get closer to the action. Sometimes this resulted in spectators being hit by the speeding racecars. Drivers and crew sometimes threw nuts, bolts, or even tools to try to slow other racers. As racecars were built with bigger engines to increase speed, crashes often resulted from not being able to stop in time because of poor brakes.

12. Big Trouble

At the supper table that evening, Henry and Robert were buzzing with stories of the day at the fair. Ma was laughing at the boys because they were so excited that they were both talking at once. Even their sister, Elizabeth, couldn't get a word in edgeways. Pa on the other hand was strangely quiet. Pa was usually the first to laugh when the boys shared their adventures of the day, but this evening he said nothing.

"What's the matter, Pa?" Ma asked. "You usually are laughing and carrying on as much as the boys, but you're sitting there as serious as if you were sitting in a town meeting."

"Seeing you mentioned it, I will be sitting in a town meeting. However, I won't be sitting by myself. Henry and Robert will be sitting with me, and I am afraid it isn't going to be a pleasant experience." The laughter of the day quickly evaporated as Pa's voice was quite serious.

"What do you mean Pa?" Robert inquired.

"Well, at the fair today a lot of other farmers and townsfolk talked with me about the mud hole. Based on those conversations, I thought I would take a closer look at it on the way home." Henry's stomach felt like it was tied in knots as his father spoke. "I found a little ditch running to the mud hole from the nearby stream bringing just enough water to keep the mud hole from drying up. I now know why the mud hole isn't drying up this summer, and I have a strong suspicion that my two boys also know why it isn't drying up. Am I right?"

Pa already knew the answer. Both boys hung their heads in shame and nodded silently at Pa's question.

Pa spoke again, his voice clearly showing his disappointment, "My boys have had some good adventures in the last few years. Adventures that were honest and fun, maybe a bit dangerous sometimes, but the adventures did not affect others. This time your adventure impacts other people in a dishonest way and that is wrong. No, you probably didn't come right out and lie about the mud hole, but your actions are deceitful or tricky, which is like living a lie. Charging money for this lie also makes it stealing. My boys lying and stealing? We will go to the next town meeting and you boys will explain what you did. You will also pay back each person you pulled from the mud hole. If the person is not from our town you will give the money to the church to help others who are in need."

The boys realized their plans had evaporated and they were feeling miserable about doing something so wrong. Henry never thought about it being lying or stealing. They were feeling worse knowing that they had just lost the trust of their father.

Pa continued, "The ditch must be stopped and the mud hole is going to need to be filled in and fixed too. Do both of you boys understand what I expect of you?"

How could one of the best days of summer change to the worst day of summer so quickly? It was like the change a summer storm with its looming clouds brings to a perfect sunny day. Henry felt a different cloud right now. The cloud of disappointing his father.

Henry spoke up softly, "Pa, I'm sorry I tricked you and everyone else into thinking the mud hole wasn't drying up. Robert did help me, but I came up with the idea for the ditch."

Robert added, "I'm sorry too."

"I forgive you," came Pa's answer, "but there are still the consequences."

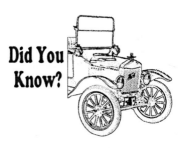

Did You Know?

The parts on automobiles have been developed over time. The dashboard of an automobile comes from the horse and carriage days. It was a board that kept stones from being tossed, or dashed, from the horse hooves at the riders in the carriage. Over time, this board moved higher, and gauges and switches were placed on it. The windshield was developed as automobiles became faster. It was needed to keep the wind off the riders in the automobile. It was often called a windscreen. In addition to keeping the wind out, the windshield also helped to keep rain away from the driver when an automobile was driven in poor weather.

13. The Town Meeting

Henry's hands were cold and white even though it was quite warm in the church. He sat in the second row from the front wishing the meeting would be over soon. How odd it occurred to Henry that the town meeting took place in the church. Not that town meetings couldn't be at the church, but that THIS meeting had to be at the church. Henry knew he had to apologize to the people of the community, but sitting in church made him realize he also needed to ask God's forgiveness for his dishonesty too.

Mr. Smith called the meeting to order and led the group through the business that needed discussed in less than 15 minutes. To Henry each of those minutes felt like an hour. When it was time for new business, Henry had a knot in his stomach.

Pa stood up and addressed the group. "I wish I could bring you good news, and in the end it will be good news, but right now it is difficult for me to admit to an activity that has impacted our small community because of poor judgment within my family. However, I believe wrongs need to be made right." Pa continued, "As many of you know, I gave my boys, Henry and Robert, the responsibility of assisting automobile owners caught in the mud hole near my farm. I have brought my two sons to explain why the mud hole near my farm has not dried up this summer."

Turning toward Henry he motioned for him to get up. "Henry, would you please explain what you know about the mud hole?"

Henry had never spoken to a group this big on an important topic. The room was silent. There were only about thirty people, but to

Henry it felt like a thousand eyes were on him as he explained about the mud hole.

"My brother and I found we could make money by pulling people out of the, uhhh, mud hole. When the mud hole started to dry up, I, ummm, came up with the idea to run water to it from the creek. It has stayed wet all summer because of the ditch we dug. I apologize for how I uhhh, tricked people, and my brother and I will be paying you back. Umm, we will also be fixing the mud hole so that people won't get stuck in it anymore."

Pa finished by explaining that the boys would be using his horse and equipment to fix the hole and make other improvements to the road as soon as possible. A few of the men attending the meeting, who were car owners, grumbled in low voices that it was about time the mud hole was talked about and that those boys deserved some strong discipline.

However, Mr. Johnson surprised everyone by standing up and stating, "I know that mud hole has caused a lot of problems this summer. I know it has for me." Nodding at Pa, Mr. Johnson went on, "I believe Walter is correct in having his boys fix the mud hole. BUT," then Mr. Johnson looked straight into Henry's eyes and said, "I will remember this day more for the guts and courage it took for a boy to stand up in a town meeting and admit his mistake and take action to correct it."

There were many grunts of approval to Mr. Johnson's comments from many of the men attending. A few people even came up to Henry and told him they were proud of him for taking responsibility for his mistake. Then, as impossible as it seemed, the meeting was over. Now it was time for action.

Did You Know?

The **Oldsmobile Runabout**, and other early automobiles, had no steering wheel. These early automobiles were basically modified carriages. Carriages were pulled by horses and could only be steered by directing the horse. The automobile, a motorized carriage, did not have a horse to follow. Early inventors developed tiller steering, similar to the steering setup of a small boat, to be used on automobiles. *Tiller steering* is a bar with a handle that is pushed from side to side to steer an early automobile. It was quickly realized that it was dangerous. If the front wheel hit a rock or a hole in the road it would turn the wheels quickly causing the bar to swing around and possibly hitting the driver or passenger and causing injury. The steering wheel quickly replaced tiller steering in the early 1900's for this reason.

Tiller Steering: A bar with a handle that is pushed from side to side to steer an early automobile.

14. Corduroy Road

Dust and dirt stuck to the sweat on the boy's bodies. Henry and Robert had sweated what seemed like buckets in the hot summer sun fixing the mud hole for the past two weeks. Two cars had become stuck while they worked, but they had to pull them out free of charge. They really missed the money they could have made.

They had used Pa's field horses and equipment to level the road. In the place where the mud hole was the worst, they had moved a large pile of new dirt. They used Pa's plow to dig a ditch on both sides of the road. This was tricky because the plow would catch on the roots of trees hidden under the soil.

"Hey Robert!" Henry leaned on his shovel and spoke to his brother. "The road that goes by

Grandpa's has logs laid on top of it where it goes through the marsh. Grandpa told me once that it was called a corduroy road because the logs made grooves like corduroy. I think we should do that over the mud hole just in case the dirt doesn't work."

"Ah Henry," complained Robert. "We've worked for almost two weeks on fixing this mud hole. I don't want to do anymore work!"

"We'll just do it from here to by that tree," Henry coaxed. "That would be maybe fifteen feet," Henry wrinkled his forehead as he tried to judge the distance and convince his brother.

Building the corduroy road added another two days to their work. Fortunately, there were a number of trees near the mud hole that fit together to make the corduroy road.

"This almost looks like a raft you would put in a pond," Robert said. "It just doesn't have any water to float."

"It's kinda like a bridge over the mud hole," Henry explained. "It just sits on the ground and you can't go under it."

"Here comes Pa!" Robert called to Henry as they were leveling the dirt over the last few feet leading up to the section of corduroy road. "Hurry up, let's see what he has to say now that we are nearly done!"

Pa either heard Robert or read his mind for when he walked up to where they were dragging the rake, he said, "You boys sure have done a nice job fixing this mud hole. I see you even went the extra mile and dug ditches on either side of the road. I'm really proud of both of you. I know it was hard work and I know it came from unusual circumstances, but I am really proud of how you two boys have shown you can be responsible."

"Pa?" Henry asked, "Did you notice we made a corduroy road like by Grandpa's house? We used logs crossways on the road so the automobiles won't sink in the mud. Grandpa gave us the idea. He told us when he first came to this town as a boy with his pa that some of the roads were in swampy sections and wagons were sinking out of sight. He told us that his pa helped make a corduroy road with logs and the wagons didn't sink in the mud anymore."

"Now that you mention it, Henry, that is a fantastic idea! We won't have to worry about our automobile getting stuck in the mud hole when we go to town," Pa teased as he turned and walked toward the house.

"Did you hear Pa?" Robert quizzed Henry. "We won't get stuck in OUR automobile. I think we're getting an automobile!"

"Now hold your horses Robert! You know Pa loves to tease. You also know that Pa calls them useless auto contraptions that make too much noise and smell up the air. He isn't getting an automobile," Henry chided as he smoothed the dirt for the last time and picked up

the rake. "Now lets get home for supper. I
could eat half a hog I am so hungry after all this
work."

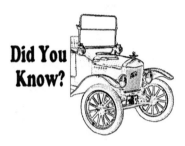

Did You Know?

Corduroy roads were built by laying logs side by side on the road in areas that were swampy or muddy. Although it was a bumpy ride, the automobile wouldn't sink down in the mud. In a way, it acted like a bridge that never left the ground. There were fewer automobiles stuck this way. This method of improving roads had been around since horse and buggy days and continued to be used until better roads were built using more current ideas and technology.

Corduroy Roads: Roads built with logs laid side by side to keep vehicles from sinking into the mud.

15. Pa's Surprise

As supper was being served, Pa acted a little more cheerful then normal. He whistled a little tune and was teasing Ma more than usual. Ma called out that supper was ready and the family sat down at the table. Everyone bowed their heads, and Pa blessed the meal. Henry noticed that Elizabeth had turned his fork and spoon upside down. When he looked at her she just stuck out her tongue and made a little face. He wrinkled his nose back at her. She usually liked to tease, the only problem was she had a hard time being teased back.

Henry's stomach was rumbling and his mind was on his food. Just as Henry stuck his first bite of potatoes in his mouth, Pa chirped up, "You know, Mary, I ran into Mr. Johnson in town today.

He wants to buy a new automobile. He told me I should buy his Model T so the boys wouldn't have to keep asking him for a ride."

The potatoes nearly stopped in the middle of Henry's throat. Was Pa feeling alright? Did his Pa have a smile on his face as he was talking about an automobile? Pa must be teasing again, Henry concluded as Pa went on.

"He told me I could have it for $400. I also saw how nice a job the boys did fixing the mud hole. You know Mary, I think the boys learned a valuable lesson. It was learned the hard way, but they learned a lot about honesty and about consequences to actions. With all the learning going on around here, I think I've been learning some too. The noisy, smelly automobile is not going to go away. I think it might be time we bought an automobile."

Henry started choking on the milk he was drinking to wash down the potatoes.

"Walter, you better not be teasing those poor boys!" Ma scolded. "They've been working so hard to correct the mischief they got into earlier this summer, and I don't think it's right to tease them like that."

"I'm not teasing this time Mary. I am quite serious about the offer. We did make almost $50 pulling stranded motorists out before I gave the job to the boys. I've also saved some money on the side. The $400 I've saved could buy a lot of things. I could buy another ten acres, but I don't have time to farm more land. It's time we bought something we could enjoy as a family. Mr. Johnson has taken very good care of that Model T and I think he is giving me a fair price. With your blessing, I'll take the boys with me to Mr. Johnson's after supper."

"Oh Walter!" tears were forming in Ma's eyes as she spoke. "I know two boys who will love it!"

Henry and Robert couldn't eat supper fast enough. It was true. Pa was going to take them and buy their first automobile. Henry had to pinch himself to make sure he wasn't dreaming.

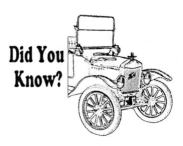

Did You Know?

Starting automobiles before the electric starter could be challenging and dangerous. The automobile had to be started by turning a *crank*, or a handle attached to the motor. When the crank turned, the parts inside the motor would begin moving causing the motor to start. The crank was often found at the front of the vehicle, which meant the driver had to be out of the car to start it. If the motor started at the wrong time, or misfired, it would cause the crank to spin the other direction and could break a hand or arm. The *electric starter* was introduced in 1912 on Cadillac automobiles and was soon available on most automobiles.

Crank: A handle used to start the engine of an early automobile.

16.   The Drive Home

Henry, Robert, and Pa arrived at Mr. Johnson's house in the early evening to see the 1910 Model T glistening in the evening light. Most Model T's were black, but Mr. Johnson kept his car so clean that the black looked as if you were looking into a midnight sky. The brass around the headlights and radiator shone so you could see yourself in them. It even had a big bulb horn. Henry squeezed it, HONK! HONK!, making Robert jump.

Pa had $400 in his pocket, which he and Mr. Johnson had agreed on for the purchase of the Model T. Mr. Johnson told them it was a touring car, meaning it had a front seat and a back seat. It also meant that the roof was made of canvas and could be pushed back and stored behind the back seat.

"Can I crank it to start it?" Henry asked as he ran to the front of the Model T.

"Wait a minute, sonny!" piped in Mr. Johnson. "You have to be careful cranking it. Many a man has broken his arm doing it wrong. Let me show you." Mr. Johnson took Henry's hand and folded the thumb into the palm of his hand. "This is important because if the motor backfires the handle jumps out of your hand instead of breaking your thumb."

"Now Walter," Mr. Johnson spoke to Henry's Pa, "This lever is called the spark lever, and this one here is the throttle. You have to adjust the spark lever just like this to get it to start."

Mr. Johnson showed Pa and the boys how to start the car, how to check the oil and gas, how to put the top up and down, and how to change the tire.

"A tire seems to go flat about once every week or two," commented Mr. Johnson.

He even gave Pa a driving lesson. When Pa needed to stop the car he called out, "WHOA BOY," as if the car was a horse.

"I don't think it heard you," Henry teased.

I've been driving horses for so long this may take a bit of getting used too," Pa remarked. "I just want to pull on this here wheel and holler, 'WHOA,' to stop it."

As they drove past their friend Charlie MacDonald's house Charlie jogged up beside the puttering automobile and hollered, "Henry and Robert, what are you doing?"

"We are buying a Model T!", exclaimed Henry.

"Ah, get a horse!", Charlie answered back causing Pa to laugh.

A short time later the breeze was blowing in their faces as Pa pointed the Model T toward home. Henry could hardly contain his excitement. His chest felt as if it were going to explode from the emotions he felt riding in the front seat of the newly purchased Model T. The toothy grin on his face showed all that Henry was feeling on the inside.

"Can I drive it, Pa?" Henry asked.

"Not yet!" Pa replied. "I'm having too much fun!"

As they rounded the corner of the dusty road near where the mud hole used to be, Henry piped up, "Watch out for the Mud hole!"

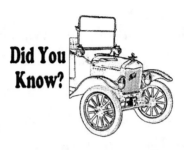

In the early days of the automobile, learning to operate one of these "motorized carriages" was a tricky process for people who had no experience with them. Farmers had trained horses to respond to word commands such as, "Whoa" to stop, "Hee" and "Haw" for left and right, or by pulling on the reins. The automobile, being a machine, did not have reins and did not respond to word commands. As a result there were many crashes for first time drivers.

Appendix:

Automobiles found in this

book

Ford Model T

Production for the Model T began in 1909 and was produced until 1927. Henry Ford used the assembly line to increase production and over 15 million Model T's were produced. This made it the most popular automobile in the world in the 1920's. It was a lightweight vehicle that was fairly reliable for its time. It had a twenty horsepower motor and a top speed of over 40 M.P.H. if you could find a road smooth enough to reach that speed. "You can get it in any color you want as long as its black", a common phrase people have said about the Model T, is only partly true. Model T's could only be ordered in the color black from 1913 To 1925. However during the beginning and end of its production it could be found in many other colors.

Oldsmobile Runabout

The Oldsmobile Runabout was a very small automobile that looked similar to a horse buggy. It was built between 1901 and 1904. It was known for the curved dashboard that formed the front of the car. This little car had a 5 HP motor and was capable of 20 mph. It had tiller steering, or a bar with a handle similar to what is used on a boat. This handle was used to steer the automobile but was quickly replaced with the steering wheel. Many automobile manufacturers used the Runabout name, but it most often referred to the little Oldsmobile. It was America's first automobile to be made in large numbers on an assembly line, even before Henry Ford and the Model T. It $650 price interestingly matched its 650 lb. weight. It became so popular that the song, "In My Merry Oldsmobile" was written about it.

Maxwell

The Maxwell was a dependable car in the early 1900's. However, it required a lot of work to keep it maintained and in good running condition. The Maxwell came only in two colors, Speedster Red and Maxwell Green. The Maxwell Green color was only available on a version built especially for doctors, the DR model. The rest were painted the Maxwell Red. It was a lightweight vehicle that was powered by a two-cylinder motor making fourteen horsepower. The Maxwell Company was taken over by Chrysler in 1924.

Pierce Arrow

The Pierce Arrow was an expensive luxury
automobile. It was well known for its reliability as
it won the Glidden Tour, a one thousand mile
race testing the reliability of early automobiles,
four years in a row. In 1909 U.S. President Taft
ordered two Pierce Arrows that were the first
automobiles to be officially used at the White

House. By 1912 it had the largest motor ever produced in an American automobile. The company went out of business during the Great Depression of the 1930's.

Peerless Green Dragon

The Peerless Green Dragon was built primarily as a racing car and had a large engine for its time. It became well known in 1904 as a racecar driven by Barney Oldfield. It was an expensive automobile and not many were made. A unique feature of this automobile was that it used solid wheels instead of the spoked wheels that were common at this time. After the Green Dragon racing car the Peerless Company focused more on luxury automobiles and were one of the first to be available with a self-starter. The Peerless Company made automobiles, from 1900-1931.

Stanley Steamer

The name of this automobile gives a hint to the engine it used. It used a steam engine. A steam engine creates heat to boil water that forms steam. The steam is put under pressure and creates the power to move the automobile. The Stanley Steamer was a very quiet automobile for its time. The biggest problem the Stanley

Steamer had was it took about fifteen minutes for the steam engine to warm up enough to move. It also needed to stop often to fill up with water to make steam. In 1906 a custom built Stanley Steamer set the land speed record of 127 m.p.h. Stanley's were built from 1899 until 1927.

Ford Model N

The Ford Model N was built from 1906 to 1908, a few years before the Model T. The two-seater automobile was simple. The convertible top and headlights were extra options. It didn't even have running boards, a step used to get into the automobile. It cost a reasonable $500 and had a new fifteen horsepower engine that would later find its way into the Model T. There were approximately seven thousand made.

About the Author

Arthur Brood resides in the Upper Peninsula of Michigan with his wife, Karen, and two daughters.

From the time he was a young child he has had a fascination with the automobile, especially the antiques. He rarely passes a car show or museum without stopping to admire the automobiles.

As for the Mud? Growing up he could be found, just as Henry and Robert, with a shovel in one hand making rivers in the mud each spring. He still looks forward to the spring thaw and grabbing a shovel.

He has been an elementary teacher since 1991. In addition to teaching school he has developed a school presentation where he enjoys acting as Henry Ford and focusing on the early automobile industry.

Photo Credits

Cover Photo, © Arthur Brood

p. 104, Model T, © Arthur Brood

p. 106, Oldsmobile Runabout, © Arthur Brood

p. 108, Maxwell, © Randy Sauder, Atlanta, GA
Used with permission

p. 110 pierce Arrow, © Robert Reenders
Used with permission

p. 112 Peerless Green Dragon, © John Filiss
Used with permission.

p. 114 Stanley Steamer, © Bryon Richmond
Used with permission.

Drawings illustrated by Lindsey Bergsma

A special thank you to Les Nyland for allowing
me to use his Ford Model T for the book cover.

Find Out More

Visit the website for information about author visits to your school, the school presentation, or other information about the author.

www.mudholebook.com

Is there a picture of you playing in the mud? Go to the website and follow the directions on how you can send in your "mud" photo for others to see.

Printed in the United States
91720LV00001B/166-264/A